Scarlett the Science Sorc...

Learns About the Digestive System

Kelly Tanner

Scarlett the Science Sorceress likes to learn new spells,
She tries her best and reads the books, but it rarely ends up well!

Last month she turned her friend into a purple pig...

... Her hair was coloured green, and her mum got *really* B

I

G

Little did she know that today was a big day.
She woke up in the morning, feeling perfectly okay.

She waltzed merrily down the stairs, and grabbed her new spell book.
She wanted to try a new spell, that she was positive would work.

Aa Bb Cc Dd Ee Ff Gg Hh Ii

The digestive system is the process of breaking down food.

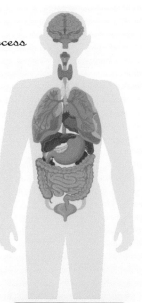

The body needs to absorb all of the good nutrients.

The body expells anything it does not need.

She had been learning all about the *digestive system* at school,
She wanted to learn some more, so that her friends would think she's cool.

With her spell book in one hand, and her wand ready to go,
She loudly read the words, and then muttered, "Oh no!"

Scarlett found herself getting smaller....

... and smaller....

... and smaller.

Scarlett found herself sitting on top the fruit and veg,
She though she could undo the magic, but things got worse instead.

Her mum walked into the kitchen, with a smile on her face.
She was feeling super hungry, and plucked a carrot from its place.

As the carrot slowly moved, from the bowl towards her face,

The **saliva glands** started pumping, it's almost like a race!

CRUNCH

CRUNCH

CRUNCH

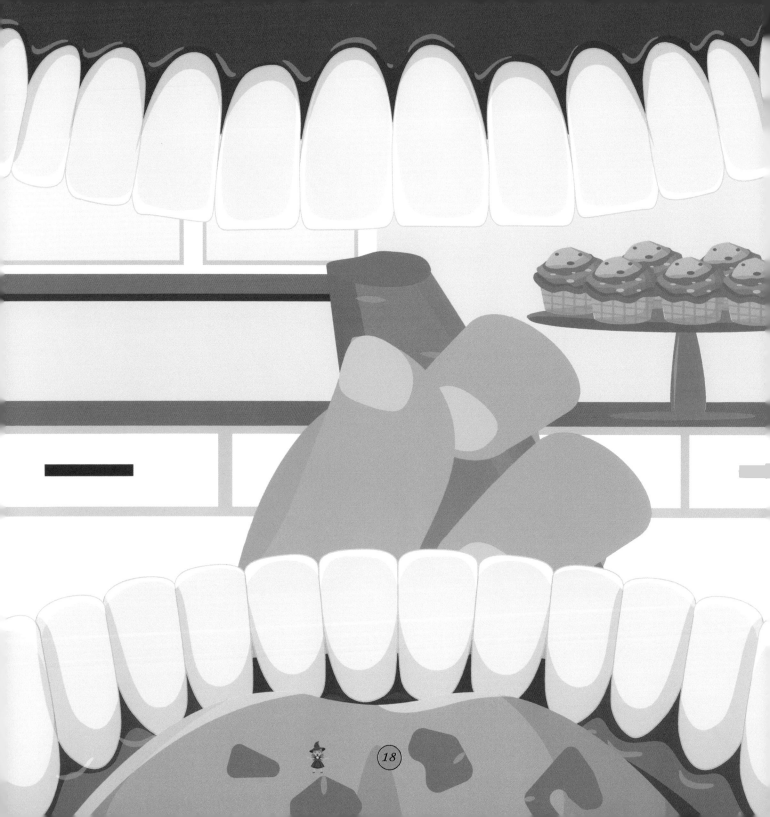

18

Scarlett's mum chewed nice and fast,
The teeth work well together,
Knowing the carrot would never last.

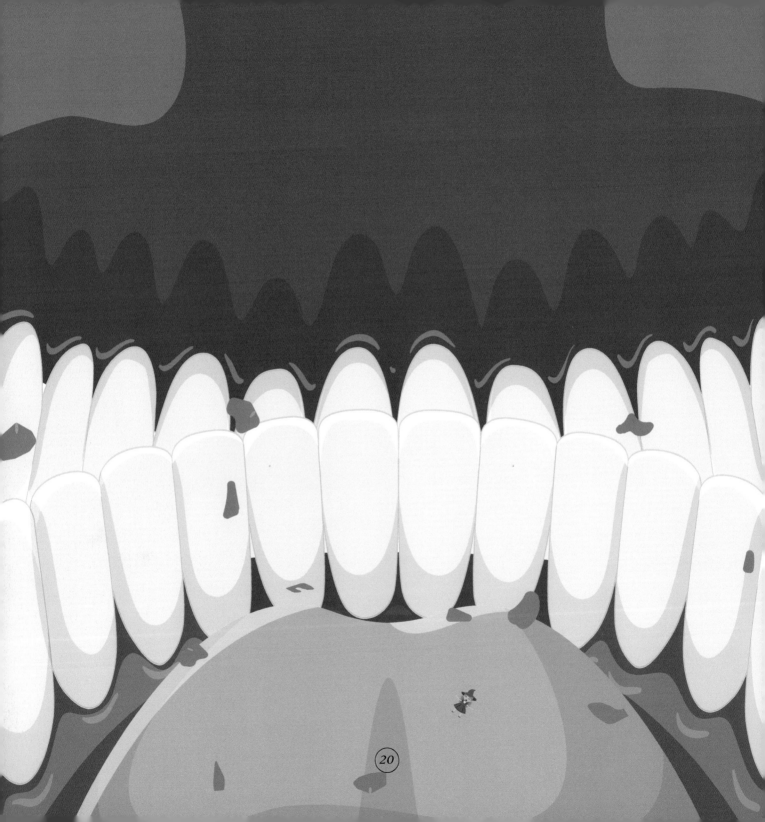

Grinding and slicing and chewing are what the **teeth** do best.

The food becomes a **bolus,** then the **tongue** can do the rest.

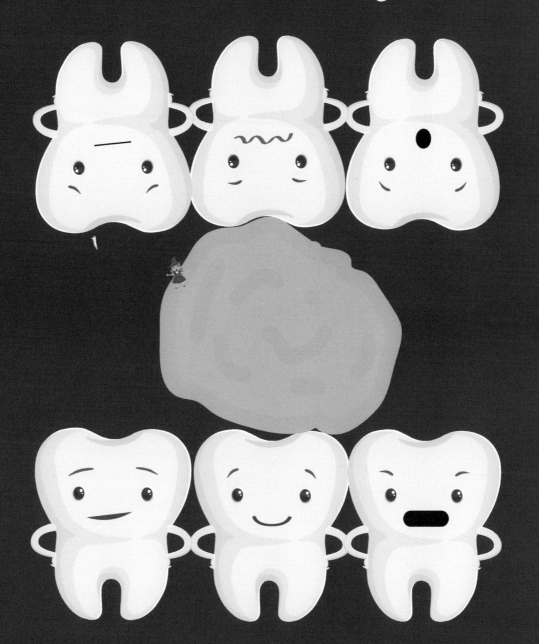

The **tongue** pushes the food to the back of the mouth, The **oesophagus** is next; the food needs to travel south.

But how can the food travel down to the **stomach**?
It needs to keep moving it cannot get stuck!

The **oesophagus**
senses a
presense of food,

The

muscles contract,

so it
gets pushed down
the tube.

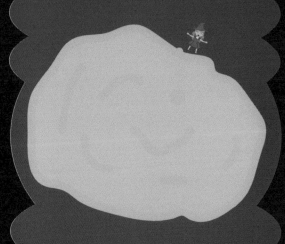

The **stomach** is strong, but it still needs the help of some $acid$,
Hydrochloric acid is released, and breaks the food into a liquid.

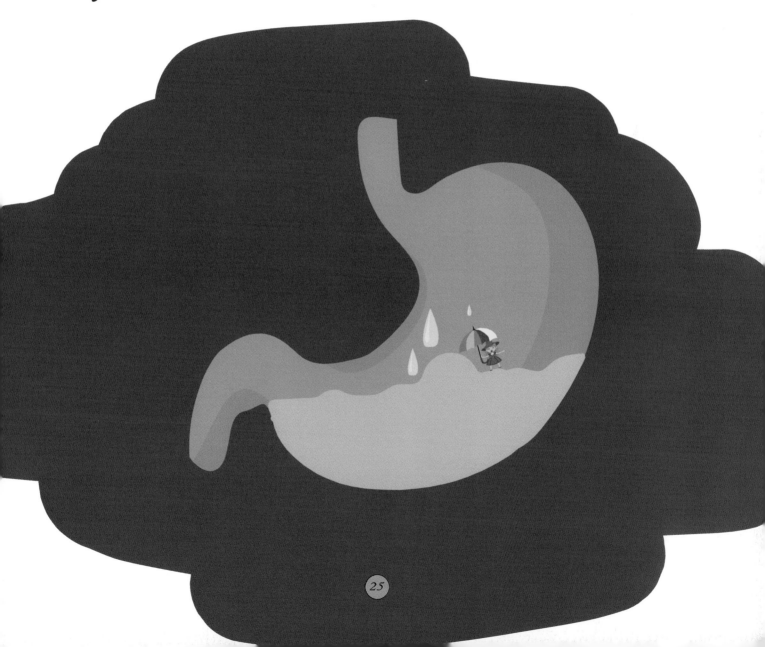

The *acid* and **hormones** need to send out a signal,

Food needs to be broken down... the body needs *bile*!

To the pancreas produces enzymes to break down
fat, protein and carbohydrates in the food.

To the liver which produces a liquid called
bile which helps to absorb fat from the food.

When the **stomach** is done breaking down the food that you've eaten, the food travels to the **small intestine** where absorption can happen!

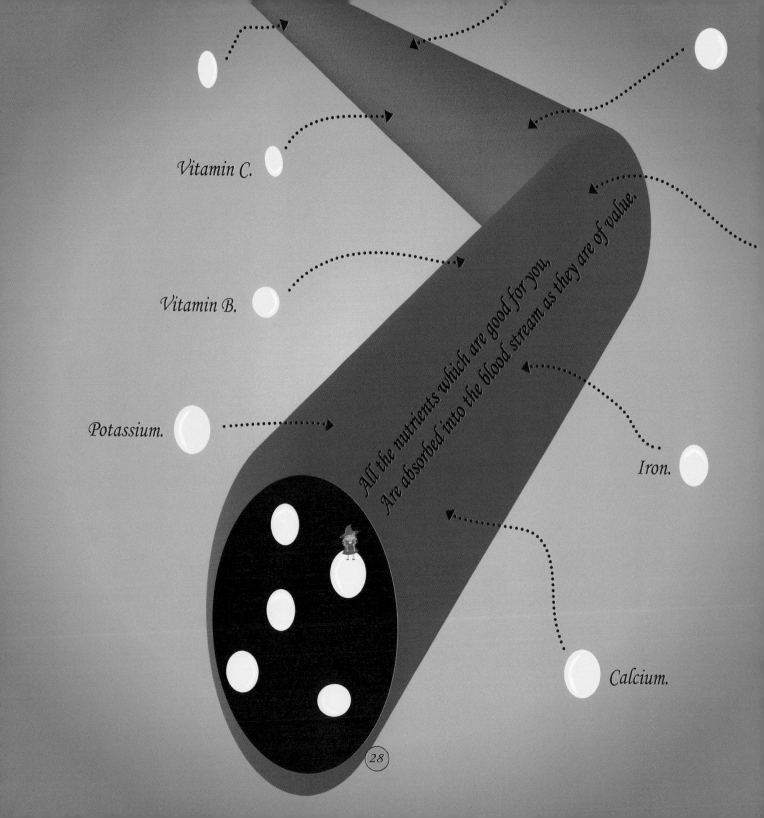

Vitamin C.

Vitamin B.

Potassium.

All the nutrients which are good for you,
Are absorbed into the blood stream as they are of value.

Iron.

Calcium.

28

Now that the small intestine has made a deduction,
The food travels to the large intestine for water absorption.

Not only is water absorbed in the large intestine, it also takes salt, minerals and vitamins.

Small intestine

Between 18-48 hours later,
The large intestine should have taken all the water.

The left over 'food' forms a **stool** in the rectum.

Your **rectum** tells your brain that it needs an extraction!

Help! We need
the toilet!

And if you're confused about what this means you should do,
It means that your bum tells your brain you need to poo!

Undo-Us Magickus!

Scarlett found herself magicked away,
She thought to herself,
"That's enough spells for one day!"
Her mum smiled down, and gave her a big squeeze,
"You know," she told Scarlett,

"The **digestive system** is a breeze!"

The End